C000146805

Broadway

15 showstoppers for keyboard

© International Music Publications Ltd
First published in 2003 by International Music Publications Ltd
International Music Publications Ltd is a Faber Music company
3 Queen Square, London WC1N 3AU

Cover Image © Corbis

Music arranged & processed by Barnes Music Engraving Ltd

Printed in England by Caligraving Ltd
All rights reserved

ISBN10: 0-571-53107-5
EAN13:978-0-571-53107-3

All Good Gifts

(FROM *GODSPELL*)

Words and Music by Stephen Schwartz

Suggested Registration: Flute
Rhythm: Ballad
Tempo: ♩ = 116

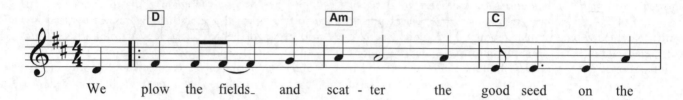

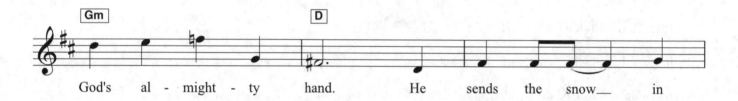

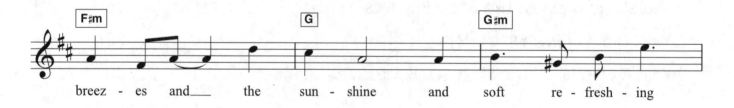

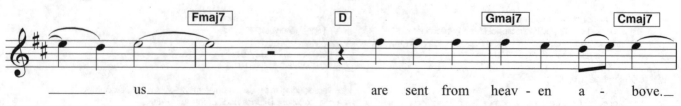

And All that Jazz

(FROM *CHICAGO*)

Words by John Kander. Music by Fred Ebb

Suggested Registration: Piano
Rhythm: Ragtime
Tempo: ♩ = 112

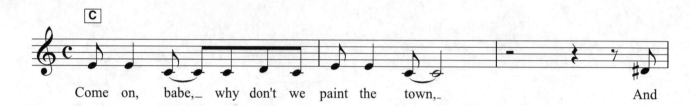

Come on, babe,_ why don't we paint the town,_ And

all that jazz!_ I'm gon-na rouge my knees_ and roll my stock-ings down_

And all that jazz! Start the car,_ I know a whoop-ee spot_ where the

gin is cold_ but the pi-an-o's hot._ It's just a nois-y hall_ where there's a

night-ly brawl And all that jazz!

Slick your hair_ and wear your buck-le shoes And all that jazz! I hear that

Fa-ther Dip_ is gon-na blow the blues And all that jazz!_

Don't Rain On My Parade

(FROM *FUNNY GIRL*)

Words by Bob Merrill. Music by Jule Styne

Suggested Registration: Trumpet
Rhythm: Bright swing
Tempo: ♩ = 132

Don't tell__ me not to__ fly, I've sim-ply got to. If some-one takes a__

__ spill, it's me and not you. Don't bring__ a-round a__ cloud To rain on my pa-

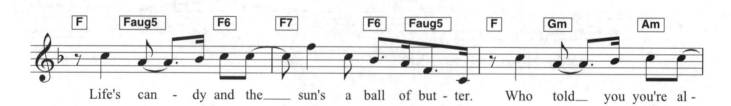

rade._____ Don't tell__ me not to__ live, just sit and put-ter.

Life's can-dy and the__ sun's a ball of but-ter. Who told__ you you're al-

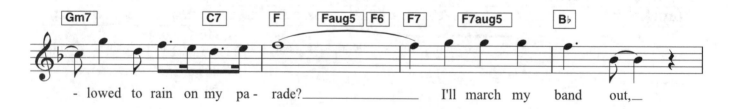

- lowed to rain on my pa-rade?_____ I'll march my band out,__

I'll beat my drum._____ And if I'm fanned out,__ Your turn at

bat, sir,__ At least I did-n't fake it, Hat, sir,__ I guess I did-n't make it!

Everything's Coming Up Roses

(FROM *GYPSY*)

Words by Stephen Sondheim. Music by Jule Styne

Suggested Registration: Trumpet
Rhythm: Bright two-beat
Tempo: ♩ = 136

Things look swell,_____ Things look great,_____ Gon - na
decks,_____ Clear the tracks,_____ We na got

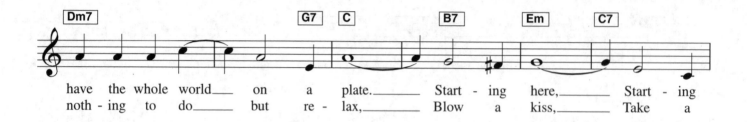

have the whole world___ on a plate._____ Start - ing here,_____ Start - ing
noth - ing to do___ but re - lax,_____ Blow a kiss,_____ Take a

now,_____ } hon - ey, Ev - 'ry - thing's com - ing___ up
bow,_____ }

ros - es!_____ Clear the ros - es!_____

Now's our___ in - ning,_____ Stand the world on its ear!

Set it spin - ning,_____ That - 'll be

9

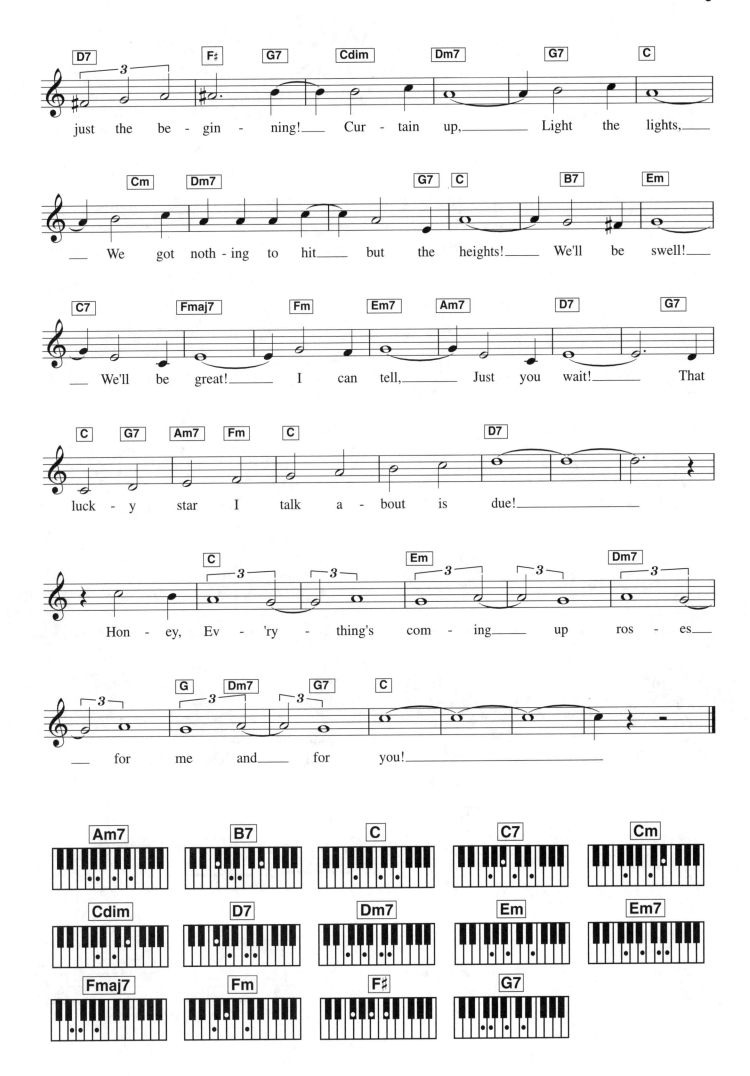

FAME!
(FROM *FAME!*)

Words by Dean Pitchford. Music by Michael Gore

Suggested Registration: Saxophone
Rhythm: Disco
Tempo: ♩ = 128

Bab - by, look___ at me___ and tell___ me what___

___ you___ see. You ain't seen___ the best___ of me yet. Give me time; I'll make

___ you for - get the___ rest. I got more___ in me,___ and you___ can set

___ it free. I can catch___ the moon___ in my hand.

Don't you know who I am?___ Re - mem - ber my name,___ fame!

I'm gon - na live___ for - ev - er. I'm gon - na learn how to fly___ high!

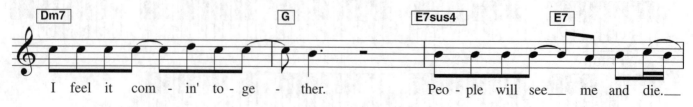

I feel it com - in' to - ge - ther. Peo - ple will see___ me and die.___

11

From This Moment On

(FROM *KISS ME KATE*)

Words and Music by Cole Porter

Suggested Registration: Violin
Rhythm: Bright show style
Tempo: ♩ = 124

If I Were A Rich Man
(FROM *FIDDLER ON THE ROOF*)

Words by Sheldon Harnick. Music by Jerry Bock

Suggested Registration: Banjo
Rhythm: Ballad
Tempo: ♩ = 112

If I were a rich man, dai - dle, dee - dle, dai - dle, dig - guh, dig - guh, dee - dle, dai - dle,

dum, All day long I'd bid - dy, bid - dy bum, if I were a wealth - y

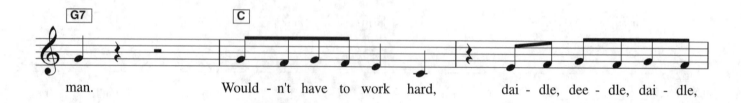

man. Would - n't have to work hard, dai - dle, dee - dle, dai - dle,

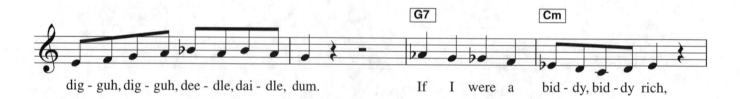

dig - guh, dig - guh, dee - dle, dai - dle, dum. If I were a bid - dy, bid - dy rich,

dai - dle, dee - dle, dai - dle, dai - dle man. I'd build a big tall house with

rooms by the doz - en right in the mid - dle of the town, A fine tin roof with

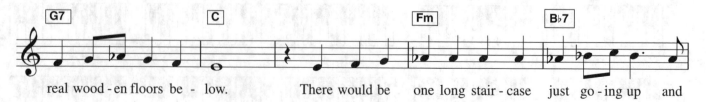

real wood - en floors be - low. There would be one long stair - case just go - ing up and

It's The Hard-Knock Life

(FROM *Annie*)

Words by Martin Charnin. Music by Charles Strouse

Suggested Registration: Clarinet
Rhythm: Show style swing
Tempo: ♩ = 144

It's the hard - knock life for us! It's the hard - knock life for us!

'Stead - a treat - ed we get tricked, 'Stead - a kiss - es we get kicked,

It's the hard - knock life! Got no folks to speak of, so,___

___ It's the hard - knock row we hoe.___ Cot - ton blan - kets 'stead - a wool,

___ Emp - ty bel - lies 'stead - a full,___ It's the hard - knock life.

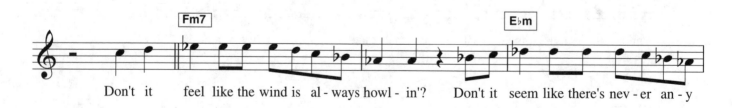

Don't it feel like the wind is al - ways howl - in'? Don't it seem like there's nev - er an - y

light? Once a day don't you want to throw the towel in? It's eas - i - er than put - tin' up a

Money Money
(FROM CABARET)

Words by Fred Ebb. Music by John Kander

Suggested Registration: Piano
Rhythm: Bright swing
Tempo: ♩ = 152

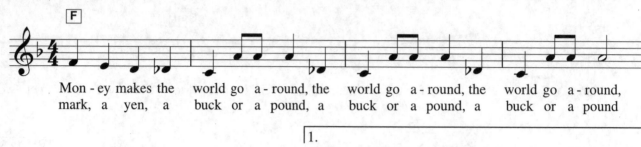

Mon - ey makes the world go a - round, the world go a - round, the world go a - round,
mark, a yen, a buck or a pound, a buck or a pound, a buck or a pound

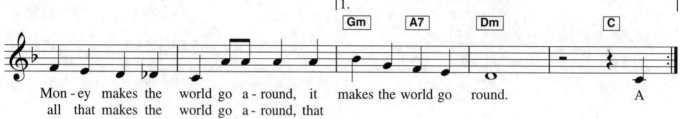

Mon - ey makes the world go a - round, it makes the world go round. A
all that makes the world go a - round, that

clink - ing, clank - ing sound can make the world go round. If you hap - pen to be

rich, and you feel like a night's en - ter - tain - ment, you can pay for a gay es - ca -

pade. If you hap - pen to be rich, and a - lone, and you need a com - pan - ion, you can

ring ting - a - ling for the maid. If you hap - pen to be rich and you find you are

left by your lov - er, tho' you moan and you groan quite a lot, you can take it on the

The Rain In Spain

(FROM *MY FAIR LADY*)

Words by Alan Jay Lerner. Music by Frederick Loewe

Suggested Registration: Violin
Rhythm: Habanera
Tempo: ♩ = 132

The rain in Spain stays main - ly in the plain.____ I think she's

got it.____ I think she's got it.____ The rain in Spain stays

main - ly in the plain.____ By George, she's got it!____ By George, she's

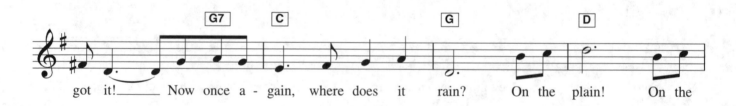

got it!____ Now once a - gain, where does it rain? On the plain! On the

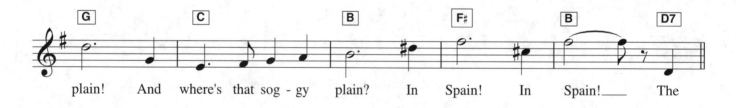

plain! And where's that sog - gy plain? In Spain! In Spain!____ The

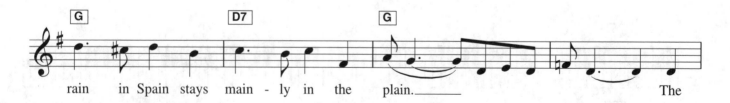

rain in Spain stays main - ly in the plain.____ The

rain in Spain stays main - ly in the plain.____ In

RAZZLE DAZZLE

(FROM *CHICAGO*)

Words by John Kander. Music by Fred Ebb

Suggested Registration: Trumpet
Rhythm: Swing
Tempo: ♩ = 104

Give 'em the old raz-zle daz-zle. Raz-zle daz-zle 'em.

Give 'em an act with lots of flash in it And the re-act-ion

will be pas-sion-ate. Give 'em the old ho-cus po-cus. Bead and feath-er 'em.

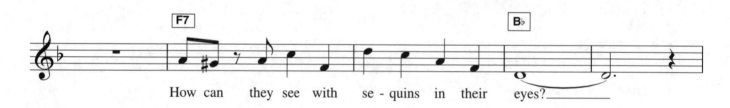

How can they see with se-quins in their eyes?_____

What if your hing-es all are rust-ing? What if in fact you're just dis-gust-ing?

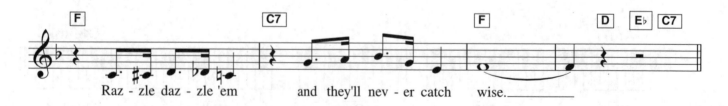

Raz-zle daz-zle 'em and they'll nev-er catch wise._____

Give 'em the old raz-zle daz-zle. Raz-zle daz-zle 'em.

THAT'S ENTERTAINMENT
(FROM *THE BAND WAGON*)

Words by Howard Dietz. Music by Arthur Schwartz

Suggested Registration: Trumpet
Rhythm: Bright show style
Tempo: ♩ = 120

The clown____ with his pants fall-ing down,___ Or the dance____

___ that's a dream of ro-mance,___ Or the scene____ where the

vil-lain is mean;___ That's en-ter-tain-ment!___ The

lights____ on the la-dy in tights,___ or the bride____

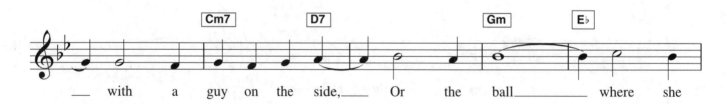

___ with a guy on the side,___ Or the ball____ where she

gives him her all,___ That's en-ter-tain-ment!___

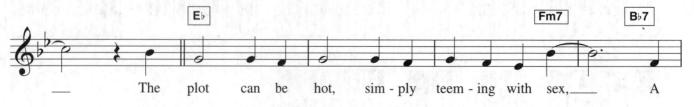

___ The plot can be hot, sim-ply teem-ing with sex,___ A

25

There's No Business Like Show Business

(FROM *ANNIE GET YOUR GUN*)

Words and Music by Irving Berlin

Suggested Registration: Brass
Rhythm: Bright show style
Tempo: ♩ = 132

Well, Did You Evah

(FROM *HIGH SOCIETY*)

Words and Music by Cole Porter

Suggested Registration: Clarinet
Rhythm: Polka
Tempo: ♩ = 72

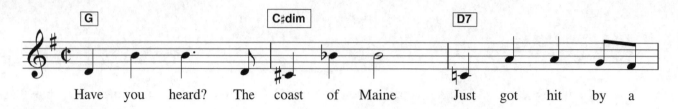

Have you heard? The coast of Maine Just got hit by a

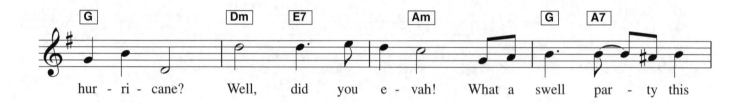

hur - ri - cane? Well, did you e - vah! What a swell par - ty this

is! Have you heard that poor dear Blanche Got run down by an

a - va - lanche? Well, did you e - vah! What a swell par - ty this

is! What Dai - quir - is! What sher - ry, please! What

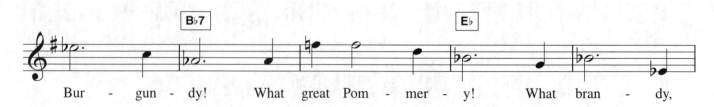

Bur - gun - dy! What great Pom - mer - y! What bran - dy,

With A Little Bit Of Luck

(FROM *My Fair Lady*)

Words by Alan Jay Lerner. Music by Frederick Loewe

Suggested Registration: Saxophone
Rhythm: Bright show style
Tempo: ♩ = 120

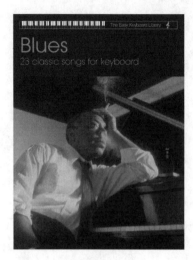
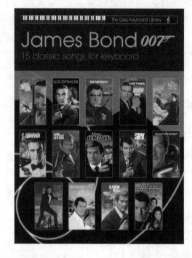

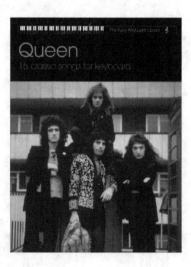